Making Connections®

Reading Comprehension Skills and Strategies

Book 1

EDUCATORS PUBLISHING SERVICE

Cambridge and Toronto

Contents

Unit 3: Main Idea

Unit 4: Compare and Contrast

Unit 1

Identifying Detail Identifying detail is finding the words that tell about something.

My Pet Elephant

What pet did the girl ask for at the end of the story?

I really want an elephant for my birthday.
I'll name my elephant Sam.
Sam can live in our big backyard!

Sam will have a long trunk.
Sam will use it to reach up high.
Sam will get cookies for me!

Sam will use that trunk like a hose.
Sam will wash the car for Mom.
Sam will wash me!

Unit 1: Identifying Detail

Mom might laugh if I ask for an elephant.
So I'll ask for a kitten.
I'll name it Sam!

Practice the Skill

Finding Details

1. Choose a word to finish the sentence.

| legs | tail | trunk | ears |

This elephant needs a ___trunk_____.

2. Draw what the elephant needs.
Color it.

3. What will Sam the elephant do?
Circle three things.

- mow the grass
- **wash me**
- wash the **car**
- read a book
- take a nap
- **get cookies**

Draw Sam doing one of them.

Check Comprehension

Where will Sam the elephant live?

Sam will live in the yard.

Giraffes

Why do giraffes have spots?

This is a giraffe.
Giraffes live in Africa.
They live in family groups called (herds.)

Giraffes are the tallest animals in the world.
Their long necks help them reach into trees.

Giraffes have very long tongues.
Their tongues help them eat leaves,
twigs, and shrubs.

Giraffes have spotted coats.
Spots help them hide from danger.

Practice the Skill

Finding Details

1. Draw and label the food a giraffe eats.

leaves

twigs

shrubs

2. It is very long. It helps a giraffe eat. What is it?

It is a giraffe's _tongue_.

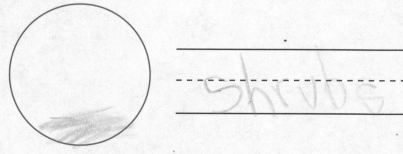

tongue	tail	spots

3. Finish the sentence.

Giraffes are the _____tallest_____ animals in the world.

Check Comprehension

1. Where do giraffes live?

_____Africa_____

2. What helps giraffes hide from danger?

_____spots_____

Vocabulary

What is the name for giraffe family groups? Find the word on page 10.

_____herds_____

Meerkats

What jobs do meerkats have?

These desert animals are meerkats.
They live in big family groups.
They sleep in dens.

Meerkats have different jobs.
This meerkat is a scout.
It tells the family if there is danger.

These meerkats are housekeepers.
They clean the family den.
Then they line the den with grass.

This meerkat is a babysitter.
It keeps the babies safe.
It feeds, teaches, and plays with them!

Finding Details

1. Where do meerkats sleep?

Meerkats sleep in _Jden_ .

2. This meerkat
   tells the family
   if there is danger.
   This meerkat is a

   scout

3. This meerkat keeps
the babies safe.
It feeds, teaches,
and plays with them.

This meerkat is a

babysitter

4. These meerkats
clean the den.
These meerkats are

housekeepers

Vocabulary

Find a word on page 16 that means

desert

"a place with little rain."

The Animal Show

Who won the animal show?

Three cheetahs lined up for an animal show.
"I will win," said the first. "I have long legs."
"I will," said the second. "I have sharp claws."
"No, I will," said the third. "I have a shiny coat."

"You all win!" said the judge.
"Every cheetah has long legs,
sharp claws, and a shiny coat!"

Practice the Skill

<u>Finding Details</u>

1. Write these details in the chart to show why each cheetah thought it would win.

a shiny coat

sharp claws

long legs

Cheetah	Detail
First	
Second	
Third	

2. Draw the cheetah you like best.

Write a detail about your cheetah.

_____

- -

_____

Vocabulary

What word on page 22 means
"not short"?

_____

- -

_____

Unit 2

Sequencing Sequencing is putting things in the order they happened.

My Soccer Team

Who gets to the game last?

I'm Kenny.

My soccer team is playing a game today!

My dad drives me in his car.

We are the first ones here.

We bring oranges and some water.

Sammy and his parents ride the bus.
They get here second.
They bring our team shirts.

Maria and her mom walk.
They get here third.
Maria brings the soccer ball.

Jane and her brother Jake ride their bikes.
They get here last.
Now our team is ready to play!

Practice the Skill

Sequence

Who gets to the game first, second, third, and last? Fill in the names.

First

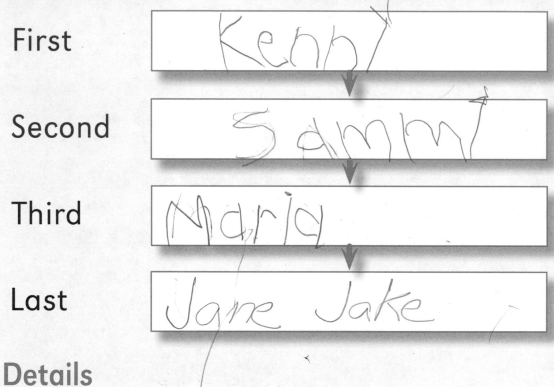

Kenny

Second

Sammy

Third

Maria

Last

Jane Jake

Details

1. Who brings what? Draw a line from each name to a picture.

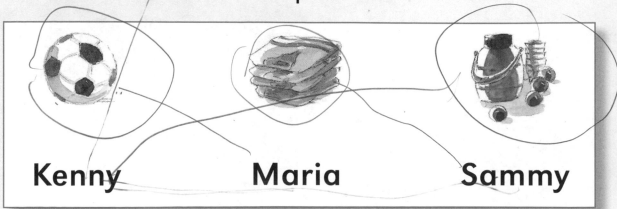

Kenny   Maria   Sammy

2. Draw pictures to show how Kenny and Jane each get to the game.

Kenny

Jane

Check Comprehension

Who travels on the bus?

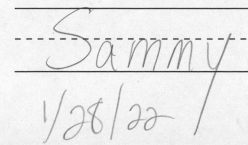

Sammy

1/28/22

Our Dog Taffy

How do they give Taffy a bath?

Taffy has been digging outside.
She is all muddy.
She needs a bath.

Taffy runs inside.
Where has she gone?
She's under the bed!
Carry her to the tub!

Wet Taffy's fur with water.
Shampoo her—look at that dirt!
Pat her dry with a soft towel.

Now Taffy is clean and dry.
But we are all muddy.
Now we need a bath!

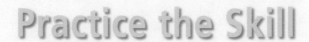

Practice the Skill

Sequence

These words tell where Taffy is.
Put them in the right order.

in the tub

under the bed

digging outside

1. *digging outside*

2. *under the bed*

3. *in the tub*

Finding Details

How did Taffy get to the tub?
Draw a picture.

Check Comprehension

Choose the best word to finish
the sentences.

clean	muddy

- At the beginning of the story,

  Taffy is _muddy_ .

- At the end, Taffy is _clean_ .

A Beautiful Sunflower

How do you grow a sunflower?

To grow beautiful sunflowers, you need a big flower pot, soil, and seeds.

Place some soil
in the flower pot.

Dig a small hole
in the soil.

Then put a
flower seed
in the hole.

Cover the seed with soil.

Give it water and sunshine every day.

Soon, a seedling will start to grow.

The seedling will grow
tall and strong.

It will grow big, green leaves and a yellow flower.
It is now a beautiful sunflower!

Practice the Skill

Sequence

Number these boxes so the steps for growing a seed are in the right order.

2 make a hole

2 water it and give it sunshine

4 cover seed with soil

1 place soil in pot

3 put seed in hole

Check Comprehension

1. What three things do you need first to grow beautiful sunflowers?

- soil

- water

- sunshine

2. What two things do the plants need every day?

- water

- sunshine

Vocabulary

Find a word on page 40 that means "very small plant."

seedling

Happy Birthday, Mom!

How do they make Mom's breakfast?

Today is my mom's birthday.
I'm making her breakfast!

First, I make toast with jam and butter.
Then Dad helps out. He makes coffee.

After that, I pour a big glass of juice.
Then I put everything on a tray.

Now breakfast is ready.
Happy birthday, Mom!

Practice the Skill

Breakfast Sequence

Number these steps.

 pour juice   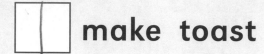 make toast

3 put everything on a tray

Draw pictures of each step to show what the girl does.

1.

2.
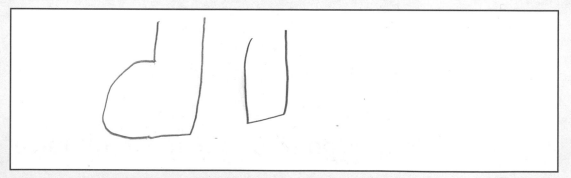

3.

Finding Details

Finish the sentences.

- I make toast with _jam_

  and _butter_ .

- Dad helps out.

  He _makes coffee_ .

Check Comprehension

Why did they make breakfast for Mom?

It was her birthday.

March 4, 2022

Unit 3

Main Idea The main ideas are the most important ideas in a text.

The Sandcastle Contest

Who won first prize?

There was a sandcastle contest at the beach.
Lots of people joined in the fun.
They used buckets and shovels to build their castles.

Navin and his dad were in the contest.
They found a flat spot on the sand.
They began to build a big sandcastle.

Navin and his dad worked hard.

They dug tunnels.

They carved windows and doors.

Then they added lots of shells and little flags.

Three people came around to pick a winner.
They looked at all the castles.
They liked the one with the shells and flags.
Navin and his dad won first prize!

Practice the Skill

Main Ideas

1. Draw a smiling face next to the most important idea of this text.

	Ideas
☺	There was a sandcastle contest at the beach.
	They used buckets.

2. Draw a smiling face next to the most important idea of page 51.

	Ideas
	They looked at all the castles.
☺	Navin and his dad won first prize.

Finding Details

1. Where was the sandcastle contest?

   The contest was at the beach.

2. What did people use to build their sandcastles?

   They used buckets and shovels.

3. How many people came around to pick a winner?

   Three people came.

Vocabulary

Find a word on page 48 that means "digging tools."

Shovels

Kinds of Art

What kinds of art does this text tell about?

There are many kinds of art.
Masks are one kind of art.
This mask is made of wood.
Leaves and paint cover it.

Puppets are another kind of art.
These puppets are called shadow puppets.
The rods on their arms and backs are
used to make them move.

Necklaces are also a kind of art.
This necklace is made of beads and string.
There are beads of many colors on the string.
They make a pattern.

Drums are a kind of art, too.
This drum is made of wood.
It has pictures painted on it.
What a beautiful kind of art!

Practice the Skill

Main Idea

1. Check the box to show the main idea of this text.

   [ ] This mask is made of wood.

   [✓] There are many kinds of art.

   [ ] Rods are used to make shadow puppets move.

2. Circle the main idea of page 55.

   The puppets have rods on their arms and backs.

   Puppets are another kind of art.

3. Circle the main idea of page 57.

   Drums are a kind of art.

   The drum has pictures painted on it.

Details

Fill in the chart.

	made of
mask	_WOOdR_
necklace	_beads_
drum	_WOOd_

Check Comprehension

Read the words. Choose the best one to finish the sentence.

string	color	necklace

The beads make a _necklace_ .

Writing

What other kinds of art do you know of? What kind is your favorite?

(ice art) painting, clay, drawing

Our Class Mural

What did the mural make the room look like?

Our class made a mural to put up on the wall.
Mr. Day put us in groups of five.
We worked together on a big sheet of paper.

My group made the sky.

Max and I spread blue paint on top of the paper.

Anna and Avi made cotton ball clouds.

Ben pasted on a yellow paper circle for the sun.

Tran's group made trees.

Amelia and Marco made the tree trunks
from cardboard rolls.

The others cut out lots of green
paper leaves.

Eddie's group made a pond and a bridge.
Emma, Eddie, and Laura made the pond
from shiny foil.
Kate and Angelo made the bridge
from craft sticks.

Pam's group made flowers.

Some of the group made the blooms
from scraps of cloth.

The rest made stems from pipe cleaners.

Mr. Day hung the mural on the wall of our room.
Our room looked very pretty.
It looked like a wonderful garden!

Practice the Skill

Main Idea

1. Check the box to show the most important idea of this text.

 Our class made a mural to put up on the wall.

 Some of the group made flowers from scraps of cloth.

2. Circle the main idea of page 61.

Anna and Avi made cotton ball clouds.

My group made the sky.

3. Circle the main idea of page 64.

Pam's group made flowers.

Some of the group made stems for the flowers.

Sequence

Write these things that Mr. Day did.

The first thing Mr. Day did was

he Put usin groups
uof five.

The last thing Mr. Day did was

he hung the mural
on the wall.

Vocabulary

Find a word on page 62 that is the name of a color.

green.

A+ 100%

A Famous Painting

What are the people doing at the river?

This painting shows people
at a river.
Some are resting on the grass.
Two others are playing
in the water.
One of them is wearing
a red hat.

Bathers at Asnieres was
painted by Georges Seurat.

There are boats on the river.
Some have sails.
The people are watching the boats.
They are having fun!

Practice the Skill

Main Idea

Check the box to show the most important idea in the text.

☑ This painting shows people at a river.

☐ There are boats on the river.

☐ People are resting on the grass.

Details

1. How many people are in the water?

   there are two people.

2. How many people do you see resting on the grass?

   There are four people.

Check Comprehension

1. List two things the people are doing.

- swimming

- resting

2. Draw a picture of the pet you see at the river.

dog

Unit 4

Compare and Contrast To compare and contrast, find what is the same and what is different.

Two Trucks

How are the lights on the trucks different?

I'm Fred.

We had show-and-tell at school on Friday.

I brought in my blue dump truck.

It has six wheels.

Allie brought a toy truck, too.

It has only four wheels.

It is red with white stripes.

Both trucks have one door that opens.

Each truck has a steering wheel and a horn.

The horn on Allie's truck does not work.

Mine does!

Both trucks have lights in front and back.
The lights on Allie's truck flash on and off.
Mine don't!
Allie and I had fun playing with our trucks.

Practice the Skill

Compare the Trucks

1. Look at the pictures of the trucks. Write one of these labels under each picture.

| Fred's truck | Allie's truck |

_____

- -

_____

_____

- -

_____

2. Check the boxes on the chart to show what each truck has.

	Fred's truck	Allie's truck
horn	✓	✓
six wheels	✓	✓
stripes	✓	✓
steering wheel	✓	✓
flashing lights	✓	✓
one door that opens	✓	✓

Check Comprehension

Whose truck has a horn that works?

Fred's truck

Vocabulary

Find a word on page 75 that means "do not."

don't

Outside My Window

How are the trees different?

When I look out my window,
This is what I see:
An apple tree that's small and young,
And a big, red maple tree.

They both need sun to help them grow,
They need the raindrops, too.
Their bright leaves float down in the fall,
In spring, they're green and new.

My cat can't climb the apple tree.
Its branches are too small.
But she climbs right up the maple tree,
And jumps onto the wall.

The apple tree has pretty white flowers.
The maple's flowers are red.
The apple tree gives us round, red fruit.
The maple gives syrup instead!

Practice the Skill

Compare the Trees

1. Draw a picture of each tree when it has flowers.

maple tree   **apple tree**

2. Write one way the maple tree is different from the apple tree.

_____

_____

_____

_____

3. What do both trees need to grow?

_____

Both trees need _____ and

_____

_____ .

Check Comprehension

1. When are the trees' leaves green?
Circle the right word.

| spring | | fall |

2. Which tree can the cat climb?

_____

_____

3. What does the apple tree give us?

_____

_____

4. What does the maple give us?

_____

_____

My Best Friend

What sport does each boy like to play?

My name is Tom.
Tim is my best friend.
We have lunch together.
I like watermelon, but Tim likes rice cakes.
We both love carrots.

I have black hair, and so does Tim.
Tim's hair is straight, and mine is curly.
We both have brown eyes.
Tim is tall. I'm not.

Tim lives on the sixth floor
of a tall building.
I live in a one—story house.
Tim just got a black kitten.
I have a white and brown kitten.

I have three big sisters.
We live with my mom and grandma.
Tim has a little sister.
They live with their mom and dad.

Tim and I like to draw pictures.
I draw cars, but Tim draws airplanes.
My favorite sport is baseball.
Tim plays basketball.

Tim and I do not really look alike.
My family is not the same as Tim's family.
We might not like all the same things,
but we really like each other!

Practice the Skill

Compare and Contrast Tom and Tim

1. Draw a line from each detail to the child it describes.

Tom

likes rice cakes

has three sisters

has black hair

has brown eyes

Tim

2. Read page 85 again. How do Tom and Tim look alike?

Tom and Tim both have

_____

_____

_____

and _____.

3. Use the words in the boxes to finish the sentences.

| watermelon | rice cakes | tall | not tall |

_____

Tom likes _____.

_____

Tim likes _____.

_____

Tom is _____.

_____

Tim is _____.

Check Comprehension

Who has a black kitten? _____

We Love Ice Cream

How are the two ice creams different?

"I love ice cream," said Dan.
"My favorite flavor is chocolate chip.
Chocolate chip tastes sweet.
It feels icy cold on my tongue.
Chocolate chip ice cream is white and brown.
It is lumpy and crunchy. Yum!"

"I love ice cream, too," said Jen.
"My favorite flavor is mango.
Mango ice cream tastes sweet and fruity.
It makes my tongue cold, too.
It is a sunny yellow color.
Mango ice cream is very smooth. Yum!"

Compare and Contrast the Flavors

1. Color each scoop of ice cream.
Then write the words that tell about it.

fruity	smooth	white and brown

crunchy	yellow	lumpy

mango

chocolate chip

2. What is the same about the
ice creams? Write two words.

_____

● -

_____

_____

● -

_____

Vocabulary

Find a word that means "a part of
your mouth."

_____

- -

_____

Writing

What is your favorite frozen treat?
Write three words to tell about it.
Then draw a picture.

Illustrations
Kate Ashforth, pp. 72–76; Geoff Cook, pp. 3, 22–23; Janine Dawson, pp. 2, 32–35; Ray Dale;
pp. 44–45; Marjory Gardner, pp. 84–90; Sally Heinrich, pp. 60–65; Vasja Koman, pp. 78–81;
Naomi Lewis, pp. 48–51; Debbie Mourtzios, pp. 26–30; Louise Pfanner, pp. 4–8.

Acknowledgements
The authors and publisher would like to thank the following for permission to reproduce the
copyright material in this book.

Photographs
akg-images/National Gallery/Erich Lessing, pp. 68–69; ANTPhoto.com/Martin Harvey, pp. 18, 21
(bottom); APL/Corbis/Gallo Images/Nigel J. Dennis, pp. 16, 20 (top); Frank Lane Picture Agency/
Frans Lanting/Minden Pictures, p. 11; Frank Lane Picture Agency/Jurgen_Christine Sohns,
pp. 10, 14; Lindsay Edwards, pp. 38, 39, 40, 41, 42 (top), 92; Lonely Planet Images/Tom Cockrem,
p. 56; Nature Picture Library/John Waters, pp. 17, 20 (bottom); Pacific Stock/Bill Backmann, p. 55;
Photolibrary.com/Mark Dyball, p. 41 (bottom); Photolibrary.com/OSF/David Macdonald, pp. 19, 21
(top); Photolibrary.com/P.Sharpe/OSF/Animals Animals-Earth Sciences, p. 13; Photolibrary.com/
Photo Researchers, Inc/George Holton, p. 54; Scotch Macaskill/Wildlife Pictures, p. 12; Stockbyte,
p. 57; Stock Photo Finder/Marianne Lannen, p. 93.